SHE THINKS

THE **ENTREPRENEURIAL WOMAN'S** GUIDE TO MOVING PAST THE **MESSY MIDDLE** AND INTO **THE EXTRAORDINARY**

WORKBOOK

ANDREA LIEBROSS

Niche Pressworks

SHE THINKS BIG WORKBOOK
ISBN: - 978-1-962956-10-9

For permission to reprint portions of this content or for bulk purchases, contact support@AndreaLiebross.com.

Published by Niche Pressworks; http://NichePressworks.com
Indianapolis, IN

The views expressed herein are solely those of the author and do not necessarily reflect the views of the publisher.

THINK big TOOLKIT

CONTENTS

ABOUT THIS WORKBOOK

Congratulations on purchasing the *She Thinks Big Workbook*! It means you're truly committed to (not just interested in!) taking the next big step on your entrepreneurial journey.

This workbook offers space for you to answer the chapter reflection questions, think about what you've learned, and jot down important notes and ideas as you read. As I mentioned in *She Thinks Big*, doing reflection exercises and journaling can make a huge difference in what you get out of the content. It's the next best thing to working directly with a coach.

Capturing your mental/internal conversations on paper can help you see and address your own mindset issues better. You will have more clarity and a far better idea how the steps in the book relate to you and your personal situation. Plus, you'll want to keep track of all your great thoughts and ideas — and who knows where they will lead you? Let's find out!

You can also find supplemental resources in my online toolkit at **AndreaLiebross.com/ toolkit** (to make things easy, just **use the QR code** in the ad in the front of this book!).

And please keep in touch! I look forward to hearing how you've grown and changed as you start Thinking Big. Let me know what you've discovered, how you've approached your journey, and where you're heading on your next great adventure! Connect with me via my website at AndreaLiebross.com, drop me an email me at support@AndreaLiebross.com, or message me on social!

Now... go do amazing things!

PART ONE

MINDSET

Chapter One *Exercises*

1 | Chapter 1 Reflection: What About You?

1 How did you feel as you read Lindsey's story? What elements can you relate to?

_____

_____

_____

_____

_____

_____

_____

2 What about Carrie's story? Was there anything in her experience you could relate to?

_____

_____

_____

_____

_____

_____

_____

3   Now, think about yourself. If I were telling your story, what would I say? What would your main issues or needs be?

_____

_____

_____

_____

_____

4   So, why did you pick up *She Thinks Big*?

_____

_____

_____

_____

_____

_____

5   What do you hope to solve by reading *She Thinks Big*? If you answer, "I don't know," that's fine. That's where a lot of my clients start out. Just tell the truth about your situation. Acknowledging the places where you say, "I do know," is a start.

> *"Just when you think you've mastered your business, the next version of the business appears."*
>
> — Andrea Liebross,
> *She Thinks Big*

_____

_____

_____

_____

_____

Chapter 1 Summary Questions

1 Looking back at the chapter and your answers to the questions, name one Big Realization you got from Chapter 1.

Example: "My Big Realization is that I'm in Parking Lot #2. I can't stop thinking about changing up my role, but I'm afraid others will judge me for it."

_____

_____

_____

_____

_____

_____

_____

2 Why is it important?

Example: "It's important to see this because I need to accept who I really am. I need to look more closely at why I'm not doing that so I can finally stop going around in circles."

_____

_____

_____

_____

_____

_____

_____

1 Chapter 1 Notes & Ideas

> "When you're spinning from one option to another and never making a decision, something has to give. It's time to ask for help."
>
> —Andrea Liebross,
> *She Thinks Big*

Chapter Two *Exercises*

 Chapter 2 Reflection: Manage Your Fears

To manage your fears, you first must identify them. As you can see by reading Brittany's story in *She Thinks Big*, sometimes that's difficult. Sometimes, the fear prevents you from even knowing it's there. Even that is scary.

However, we're going to try to uncover some of the things you're dealing with so you can turn fear into fuel. With that in mind, look back at the nine common fears and see if you can relate to any of them.

1 What am I most afraid of? (There may be more than one thing.)

_____

_____

_____

_____

_____

2 How has my emotional state (i.e., feelings) affected my success? What areas of my life are suffering due to these feelings?

_____

_____

_____

_____

_____

3 How is my fear affecting my behavior (i.e., actions)? What have I been avoiding? What have I been doing more of — passive action, busy work, or just finding escape activities?

4 If I could sprinkle my own magic fairy dust over my life and make everything how I want it to be, what's the biggest thing I would change right away?

2 | Chapter 2 Summary Questions

1 Looking back at the chapter and your answers to the questions, name one Big Realization you got from Chapter 2.

Example: "My Big Realization for Chapter 2 was reading the client's story and seeing that there are other people out there with the same problems I'm having! That was a surprise to me."

_____

_____

_____

_____

_____

_____

2 Why is it important?

Example: "It's important to know I'm not alone! And now, I have more hope that there's a solution to my problem, too."

_____

_____

_____

_____

_____

_____

_____

_____

> *"Being an entrepreneur is a journey in personal development disguised as an entrepreneurial adventure."*
>
> —Andrea Liebross, *She Thinks Big*

Chapter Three *Exercises*

3   Chapter 3 Reflection: Your Limiting Beliefs

1   Think about a problem you're dealing with. Write down all your thoughts about it — why you need to solve the problem, why you feel you can't or shouldn't, what is holding you back from taking action, etc. Make your thoughts as detailed as they need to be.

_____

_____

_____

_____

_____

Now, look at what you wrote and ask yourself a few questions.

2   Do my thoughts inspire me to move toward what is significant and valuable to me? Or are they keeping me stuck or moving me away from something of value? (I especially like this one because every thought you have is either taking you closer to or farther from your best self and your best life.)

_____

_____

_____

_____

_____

3 Do my thoughts serve me? Are they useful? Why or why not?

4 If you answered NO to any of those questions, shift gears and attempt to shift each limiting belief into a liberating truth. What would be different if that liberating thought were true? (We'll talk more about this in a coming chapter.)

3 **Chapter 3 Summary Questions**

1 Looking back at the chapter and your answers to the questions, name one Big Realization you got from Chapter 3.

_____

_____

_____

_____

_____

_____

_____

_____

_____

2 Why is it important?

_____

_____

_____

_____

_____

_____

_____

_____

_____

_____

_____

Chapter 3 Notes & Ideas

> *"Limiting beliefs hold you back more frequently and more deeply than any external factor."*
>
> —Andrea Liebross, *She Thinks Big*

Chapter Four *Exercises*

4 Chapter 4 Reflection: Make That Decision!

1 Identify one challenge or situation you need (or want!) to move forward on but just can't seem to take that next step.

_____

_____

_____

_____

_____

_____

2 Using the four questions in this chapter, find your commitment level. Are you interested or committed?

_____

_____

_____

_____

_____

_____

_____

_____

_____

3   If you're interested, do you even want to be committed? If so, what would it take to get to commitment? And what would you gain or what would change if you were committed?

4   If you're committed, then what is holding you back from moving forward and deciding the next best steps? Is it fear or something else? Message me on one of my social media accounts (see AndreaLiebross.com) or email me at support@AndreaLiebross.com and tell me about it!

> If you're still hesitating on the decision, keep reading, and think about it. As you read more, you may get more ideas for the best way to think about this decision.

4 Chapter 4 Summary Questions

1 Looking back at the chapter and your answers to the questions, name one Big Realization you got from Chapter 4.

_____

_____

_____

_____

_____

_____

_____

2 Why is it important?

_____

_____

_____

_____

"When you're committed, your desire for the result, not your love for the activity, drives you to do the activity."

—Andrea Liebross, *She Thinks Big*

_____

_____

_____

_____

4 Chapter 4 Notes & Ideas

> *"Not deciding is a decision*
> *— a decision to just stay interested."*
>
> —Andrea Liebross, *She Thinks Big*

PART TWO

big
PLANS

Chapter Five *Exercises*

5   Chapter 5 Reflection: Your Snapshot

1   Refer back to the Assess Your Seven Life Facets section in this chapter and answer the questions to create your own snapshot. (You can **use the assessment worksheet at www.AndreaLiebross.com/toolkit to do the assessment**.)

_____

_____

_____

_____

_____

_____

2   When you visualized the Seven Facets as people, what qualities about these people are affecting your relationships with them? Are these relationships working for you, and if not, what needs to change?

_____

_____

_____

_____

_____

_____

_____

3 What thoughts from your Mental House are getting in the way of you taking each facet to a 10?

_____

_____

_____

_____

_____

_____

4 If each facet was a 10, how would you feel? What would be possible in your life and business?

_____

_____

_____

_____

_____

_____

_____

_____

_____

_____

_____

> *"When you're thinking small, you're lost in details and trivia that eat up your day. These details create mental clutter."*
>
> — Andrea Liebross,
> *She Thinks Big*

5 | Chapter 5 Summary Questions

1 Looking back at the chapter and your answers to the questions, name one Big Realization you got from Chapter 5.

_____

_____

_____

_____

_____

_____

_____

_____

2 Why is it important?

_____

_____

_____

_____

_____

_____

_____

_____

_____

5 Chapter 5 Notes & Ideas

> *"Thinking Big is also being smart about what you allow into your mind."*
>
> —Andrea Liebross, *She Thinks Big*

Chapter Six *Exercises*

6 | **Chapter 6 Reflection: Start Liberating Yourself**

1 Identify three limiting beliefs and shift them into liberating truths. (This can be hard. Message me at support@AndreaLiebross.com or through one of my social media accounts if you need help.)

_____

_____

_____

_____

_____

_____

2 What projects or tasks did you put into the Urgent/Important box in the Eisenhower Matrix? How will they give you margin to do your Big Planning?

_____

_____

_____

_____

_____

_____

3   What projects or tasks are in the Not Important boxes? And why?

_____

_____

_____

_____

_____

_____

_____

4   How would it feel to delegate or eliminate any of the projects in the Not Important boxes? If you have tried to delegate in the past and it didn't work, why? Do you notice any fears or limiting beliefs around delegating?

_____

_____

_____

_____

_____

_____

_____

> If you're still having trouble making these decisions, you may want to think about working with a coach who can help you figure out what's going on.

6 Chapter 6 Summary Questions

1 Looking back at the chapter and your answers to the questions, name one Big Realization you got from Chapter 6.

_____

_____

_____

_____

_____

_____

_____

2 Why is it important?

_____

_____

_____

_____

_____

_____

_____

_____

_____

_____

_____

_____

"Learn to recognize fact from fiction — it will change your life."

—Andrea Liebross,
She Thinks Big

6 Chapter 6 Notes & Ideas

> "You not only cannot afford to stay stuck in your parking lot, you owe it to everyone else to get unstuck as soon as you can."
>
> —Andrea Liebross,
> *She Thinks Big*

Chapter Seven  Exercises

 7 | **Chapter 7 Reflection: Your Big Picture**

1 Who is the Future You? What does she think and feel? How is she different from Present You?

_____

_____

_____

_____

_____

_____

_____

2 What limiting beliefs sprang to mind as you created your power sentence, 10-year vision, and three-year target? Push yourself to shift them into more empowering thoughts.

_____

_____

_____

_____

_____

_____

3 What can you do to step more fully into your power sentence? How can you use it to fuel your motivation each day? Pick one way to use your power sentence and start doing it right away. Not tomorrow — today.

4 What does it look and feel like to be "all-in"? Does having an "all-in" mindset scare you or excite you? Why?

7 | **Chapter 7 Summary Questions**

1 Looking back at the chapter and your answers to the questions, name one Big Realization you got from Chapter 7.

_____

_____

_____

_____

_____

_____

_____

_____

2 Why is it important?

_____

_____

_____

_____

_____

_____

_____

_____

> *"There is no doubt about it; a 10-year vision is larger than life."*
>
> —Andrea Liebross,
> *She Thinks Big*

Chapter Eight *Exercises*

8   Chapter 8 Reflection: Your Action Plan

1   When someone says "goals," do you feel defeated or energized? Does the word "goals" work for you? Is the word "priorities" a better fit? Why or why not?

_____

_____

_____

_____

_____

2   Create your Belief Plan.

_____

_____

_____

_____

_____

_____

_____

"As an entrepreneur, you're not only a power consumer; you're a power generator."

—Andrea Liebross,
She Thinks Big

_____

_____

_____

_____

3 Create your one-year goals using the SMARTER format. Create your 90-day focus areas within your Zone of Extraordinary Achievement. See **AndreaLiebross.com/toolkit** for more resources.

4 Look at last week. Did the way you used your time fuel your 90-day focus areas? What can you do differently this week to have better alignment?

5 Where do you need new or better systems? If you had them, what would be possible? Identify the next best step in creating new or better systems.

1 Looking back at the chapter and your answers to the questions, name one Big Realization you got from Chapter 8.

_____

_____

_____

_____

_____

_____

_____

_____

_____

_____

2 Why is it important?

_____

_____

_____

_____

_____

_____

_____

_____

_____

_____

_____

8 Chapter 8 Notes & Ideas

PART THREE

big
RESULTS

Chapter Nine *Exercises*

9 | **Chapter 9 Reflection: Find Your Freedom**

1 What kinds of freedom do you crave most — time, money, relationships, or brain power? Why?

_____

_____

_____

_____

_____

_____

_____

2 What relationships are restricting or no longer serving you? Why are you holding onto them? If you let go of them, what freedoms would be available to you?

_____

_____

_____

_____

_____

_____

_____

_____

3 If you had these freedoms, what would be possible in your life and business? How would having those possibilities affect your sense of fulfillment?

_____

_____

_____

_____

_____

_____

_____

4 What would Future You tell Present You to do today to start creating more freedom?

_____

_____

_____

_____

_____

_____

_____

_____

_____

> _"How to have a relationship is often far more important than whether to have it."_
>
> —Andrea Liebross,
> _She Thinks Big_

9 Chapter 9 Summary Questions

1 Looking back at the chapter and your answers to the questions, name one Big Realization you got from Chapter 9.

_____

_____

_____

_____

_____

_____

_____

_____

2 Why is it important?

_____

_____

_____

_____

_____

_____

_____

_____

_____

9 **Chapter 9 Notes & Ideas**

Chapter Ten *Exercises*

10   Chapter 10 Reflection: Finesse Your Stress

1   Think back to the challenge or situation you identified in Chapter 3. Looking at the seven assumptions about Stuck Stress, are any of these assumptions around that situation preventing you from moving into Progress Stress?

_____

_____

_____

_____

_____

_____

2   What will it take to move into Progress Stress?

_____

_____

_____

_____

_____

_____

_____

3 Have you started Thinking Big as you're reading this book? If so, how?

4 What are the most important things you've realized about yourself during this process? What has surprised you the most about yourself?

10 Chapter 10 Summary Questions

1 Looking back at the chapter and your answers to the questions, name one Big Realization you got from Chapter 10.

_____

_____

_____

_____

_____

_____

_____

_____

_____

2 Why is it important?

_____

_____

_____

_____

_____

_____

_____

_____

_____

_____

10 Chapter 10 Notes & Ideas

> "An entrepreneurial soul needs challenge, risk, and exploration. You can't have those and cling to security, too."
>
> —Andrea Liebross, *She Thinks Big*

Chapter Eleven  Exercises

Chapter 11 Reflection: Go from "Either/Or" to "And"

1 Write down five things you have either/or beliefs about. For example:

"Marriage is good."   *"Being single is bad."*

"Always being there for my friends is good."   *"Taking time for myself is bad."*

_____   _____

_____   _____

_____   _____

_____   _____

_____   _____

_____   _____

2 Now, for each, restate it with AND. For example:

"Marriage is good and bad."   *"Being single is good and bad."*

"Always being there for my friends is good and bad."   *"Taking time for myself is good and bad."*

_____   _____

_____   _____

_____   _____

_____   _____

_____   _____

3 What needs to happen for you to believe the AND statements? What new thoughts will you have to borrow from?

_____

_____

_____

_____

_____

_____

_____

_____

_____

_____

> *"This is the secret successful businesswomen get. They realize they're never actually going to be finished. There's always another set of challenges that come from solving the ones they're working on now."*
>
> —Andrea Liebross,
> *She Thinks Big*

4 How will shifting to AND statements change your outcome?

_____

_____

_____

_____

_____

_____

_____

_____

_____

_____

_____

Chapter 11 Summary Questions

1 Looking back at the chapter and your answers to the questions, name one Big Realization you got from Chapter 11.

_____

_____

_____

_____

_____

_____

_____

_____

_____

_____

2 Why is it important?

_____

_____

_____

_____

_____

_____

_____

_____

_____

> *"The 'right/wrong' mentality is a huge source of Stuck Stress. It keeps you paralyzed from moving toward opportunity."*
>
> —Andrea Liebross, *She Thinks Big*

11 Chapter 11 Notes & Ideas

Chapter Twelve *Exercises*

 Chapter 12 Reflection: You're Worth It

1 What is important to you about doing this work — not just as you read the book and do these exercises, but throughout the rest of your life?

_____

_____

_____

_____

_____

2 What would your life and business look and feel like if you started Thinking Big today? What would be possible that today seems impossible?

_____

_____

_____

_____

_____

> For more on why the process outlined in *She Thinks Big* is so important, listen to my podcast, *Time to Level Up* — specifically episode 96,
> "The Difference Between Doing Work and Doing the Work That's Worth Doing."
> https://AndreaLiebross.com/doing-work-and-doing-the-work-thats-worth-doing/

3   Who is on your "Board of Directors"? Who supports you in your quest for growth? Do you need some new members to fill the seats?

_____

_____

_____

_____

_____

_____

_____

_____

_____

> "'Work worth doing' is work that happens first in your head and heart. It's learning who you're being and becoming and what you're feeling."
>
> — Andrea Liebross, *She Thinks Big*

_____

_____

_____

_____

_____

_____

_____

12 Chapter 12 and Book Summary Questions

1 What is the biggest change in your mindset after reading the book and answering the questions in this workbook?

_____

_____

_____

_____

_____

_____

_____

_____

2 How will this change impact the way you approach your next big move in your life and/or business?

_____

_____

_____

_____

_____

_____

_____

_____

_____

3 If you could tell other entrepreneurial women one "most important" thing you've gleaned from having this new mindset, what would it be? How can you support them in their own Big Thinking?

_____

_____

_____

_____

_____

_____

_____

_____

_____

_____

_____

Don't forget to download the other resources from my website at AndreaLiebross.com/toolkit if you haven't already done so.

I believe in you more right now than you believe in yourself. Going it alone is hard. And even if you're not physically alone, you most likely are alone in your thoughts. You're stuck in your own peanut butter jar, and I'm here to help you read the label. Connect with me via my website or social media — or email me at support@AndreaLiebross.com.

Let's do this!

Chapter 12 Notes & Ideas

ABOUT THE AUTHOR

Andrea Liebross is a coach, speaker, author, and host of the *Time to Level Up* podcast. She's known for helping high-achieving entrepreneurial women make the shift from overwhelm to freedom so they stop thinking small and start thinking big. Through her work, she guides bold, ambitious women to create their own secret sauce for success by combining two ingredients: the right mindset and solid systems.

Andrea shows women how to shift from believing what they want is impossible, complex, and daunting to possible just by simplifying, making things doable and FUN (even the systems), and adding a bit of confidence. Andrea's signature process leads them to find success on their OWN terms and, ultimately, to joy and freedom in life and business.

After graduating from Dartmouth College and marrying the guy who lived down the hall, Andrea and her husband moved from the Northeast (go Red Sox) and settled in Indianapolis. Over the last few decades, Andrea started three successful businesses and became a certified business and life coach, all while raising two kids (at the time of writing, ages 22 and 19) and two giant Leonbergers (they might be more work than the kids!).

DOWNLOAD YOUR

THINK *big* TOOLKIT

For MUST-HAVE planning tools that work seamlessly with the book to help you **stop overthinking and make confident, quick decisions to get what you want — every single time,** download my Think Big Toolkit. (I couldn't fit everything in the book!)

AndreaLiebross.com/toolkit

Made in the USA
Middletown, DE
05 December 2023

43470651R00038